PHILIP GLASS

The Not-Doings of an Insomniac

(in the Form of a Partita in Seven Movements for Double Bass)

with poetry/words by
Lou Reed, Yoko Ono, Patti Smith, David Byrne,
Laurie Anderson, Leonard Cohen, and Arthur Russell

Dunvagen Music Publishing
/ Chester Music Ltd.

Composed for Robert Black

The Not-Doings of an Insomniac

Philip Glass

Small Town

Lou Reed and John Cale

When you're growing up in a small town
You know you'll grow down in a small town
There is only one good use for a small town
You hate it and you know you'll have to leave.

1. Not Dreaming

copyright © 2018 Dunvagen Music Publishers

Telephone Song

Laurie Anderson

Hi. How are you? What are you doing? Yeah, I know, it's kind of noisy here. There's kind of a party going on. Why don't you just come over? Just put on your coat and call a cab and come over. Yeah, I know you're asleep —but it's really fun—you'd have a really good time. Just put on your shoes and call a cab and come over. No, he's not here. Well, maybe he's here— maybe he's not here. What's the difference? Yeah, I know it's Brooklyn. Yeah, well, what's thirty bucks? It's two nights. OK. OK. Listen, I'm sure I could get you in.

2. Not Tasting

(a little slower)

Shine, Shine

Yoko Ono

Look at the highrises around you.
Incredible! Impossible!
Let everything in your room shine and sparkle.
Sparkling phone, sparkling floor,
Sparkling glasses, sparklings hats.
Start thinking what else.
Everything that sparkles brings you a sparkling life.
Sparkling eyes, sparkling belly button, sparkling legs.
Yes, dear. i ii iii

3. Not Smelling

Neighborhood

David Byrne

Funky beats, Barrow Street
Walking with your dog

I see you, You see me
Then we stop & talk

Later on, some café
Thinking what you said

Children laugh, telling jokes
Till their eyes are red

The people feel so good
Say boy, say girl
All in my neighborhood
Say boy, say girl
We got peace, love & monkey business
Gonna reach the very top
There'll be pride, hope & Sunday mornings
All the things I'm thinking of
We could change the world
In the night while we are sleeping
The Power's in my neighborhood

Liquor stores, stop & shop
Old folks sit outside
Restaurants — Laundromats
She's still on my mind

April, May, June, July,
August comes around
Pretty soon, a year's gone by
And we're still hanging out.

4. Not Hearing

I Wonder How Many People in this City

Leonard Cohen

I wonder how many people in this city
live in furnished rooms
Late at night when I look out at the buildings
I swear I see a face in every window
looking back at me
and when I turn away
I wonder how many go back to their desks
and write this down.

5. Not Seeing

Excerpt from "Babel"

Patti Smith

Everything comes down so pasteurized
everything comes down 16 degrees
they say your amplifier is too loud
turn your amplifier down
are we high all alone on our knees
memory is just hips that swing
like a clock
the past projects fantastic scenes
tic/toc tic/toc tic/toc
fuck the clock!

6. Not Touching

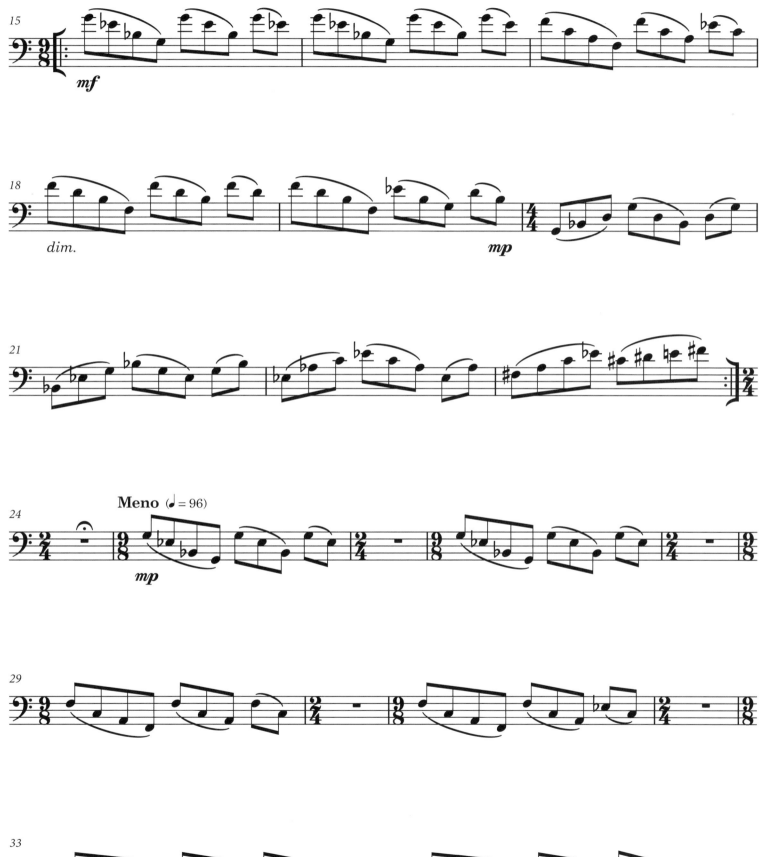

Nobody Wants a Lonely Heart

Arthur Russell

Now as you eat
Don't think of the one you love
And on the street
Don't look at the sky above
If there's no one home
Don't expect nothing
'Cause nobody wants a lonely heart

Now like a dog
Who's homeless and can't be sleeping
Like a log
He knows that he's best off keeping out of sight
Don't expect nothing
'Cause nobody wants a lonely heart

And in the door
There's nobody coming through it anymore
But I'm looking through it to some other way
Don't expect nothing
'Cause nobody wants a lonely heart
Nobody wants a lonely heart

7. Not Beginning, Not Ending

15

Smalltown
Words and music by Lou Reed and John Cale
Copyright © 1990 Metal Machine Music and John Cale Music, Inc.
All Righs on behalf of Metal Machine Music administered by Sony/ATV Music Publishing LLC,
424 Church Street, Suite 1200, Nashville, TN 37219
International Copyright Secured. All Rights Reserved.
Reprinted by Permisson of Hal Leonard LLC

Telephone Song
by Laurie Anderson
© Difficult Music. Used by Permission.

Shine, Shine
by Yoko Ono
© Ono Music administered by Downtown DMP (BMI). Used by Permission.

Neighborhood
Words and Music by David Byrne
© 2001 Moldy Fig Music
All Rights on Behalf of Moldy Fig Music administered by Warner-Tamerlane Publishing Corp.
All Rights Reserved
Used by Permission of Alfred Music

I Wonder How Many People in this City
by Leonard Cohen
© Old Ideas, LLC. Used by Permission.

excerpt from **Babel**
by Patti Smith
© Patti Smith. Used by Permission.

excerpt from **Nobody Wants a Lonely Heart**
by Arthur Russell
© Domino Publishing Company of America, Inc. Used by Permission.